Anne Geddes

Down in the Garden

Book of Days

HEADLINE

First published in Great Britain in 1997
by HEADLINE BOOK PUBLISHING

10 9 8 7 6 5 4 3 2 1

ISBN 0 7472 1890 0

Designed by Jane Seabrook
Produced by Kel Geddes
Typeset by Image Design
Images first published in *Down in the Garden*
Colour separations by Image Centre

Printed and bound in Hong Kong by South China Printing Co Ltd

HEADLINE BOOK PUBLISHING
A division of Hodder Headline PLC
338 Euston Road
London NW1 3BH

Anne and Lilly

"I am frequently asked why I photograph babies so often, and where my ideas come from. Little babies are indeed my inspiration, and I cannot imagine a photographic life without them playing a major part in it. Where this special love for babies comes from I cannot tell you, and I have spent much time searching for an answer myself. All I know is that they are perfect little human beings in their own way, and we should all take time to cherish them, especially while they are very small." Anne Geddes

These words are taken from the foreward to Anne's latest book *Down in the Garden* . They give an insight to the special magic that Anne is able to create in her photographic works.

A visit to Anne's garden and her unique vision of all that is beautiful is a journey that shouldn't be missed.

JANUARY

1

2

3

4

5

6

7

JANUARY

8

9

10

11

12

13

14

15

16

17

18

19

20

21

January

22

23

24

25

26

27

28

29

30

31

NOTES

February

1

2

3

4

5

6

7

FEBRUARY

8

9

10

11

12

13

14

15

16

17

18

19

20

21

February

22

23

24

25

26

27

28

29

NOTES

MARCH

1

2

3

4

5

6

7

MARCH

8

9

10

11

12

13

14

15

16

17

18

19

20

21

March

22

23

24

25

26

27

28

29

30

31

NOTES

APRIL

1

2

3

4

5

6

7

April

8

9

10

11

12

13

14

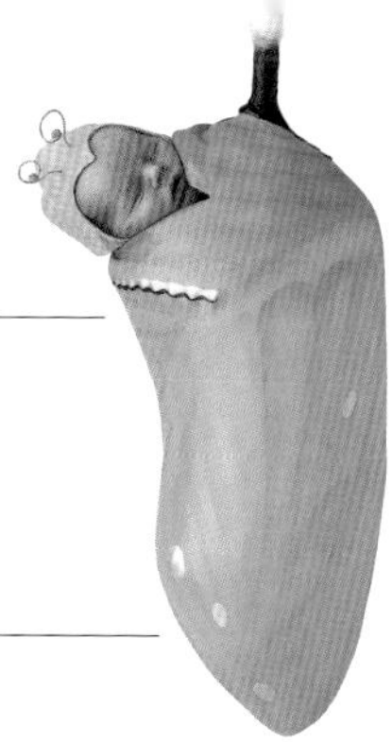

15

16

17

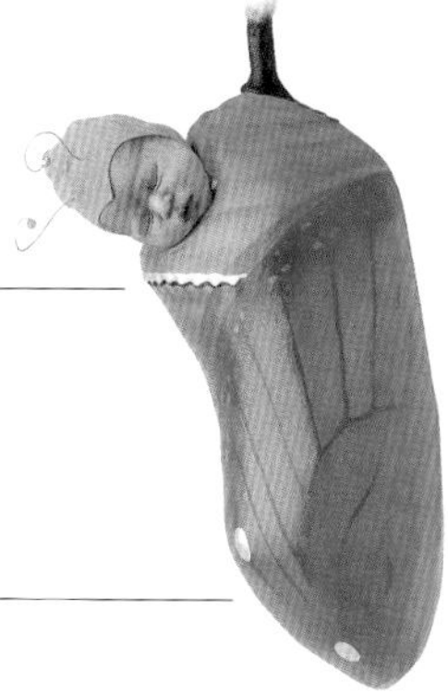

18

19

20

21

April

22

23

24

25

26

27

28

29

30

NOTES

May

1

2

3

4

5

6

7

MAY

8

9

10

11

12

13

14

15

16

17

18

19

20

21

May

22

23

24

25

26

27

28

29

30

31

NOTES

JUNE

1

2

3

4

5

6

7

JUNE

8

9

10

11

12

13

14

15

16

17

18

19

20

21

June

22

23

24

25

26

27

28

29

30

NOTES

July

1

2

3

4

5

6

7

ANNE GEDDES

July

8

9

10

11

12

13

14

15

16

17

18

19

20

21

July

22

23

24

25

26

27

28

29

30

31

NOTES

August

1

2

3

4

5

6

7

AUGUST

8

9

10

11

12

13

14

15

16

17

18

19

20

21

AUGUST

22

23

24

25

26

27

28

29

30

31

NOTES

SEPTEMBER

1

2

3

4

5

6

7

September

8

9

10

11

12

13

14

15

16

17

18

19

20

21

SEPTEMBER

22

23

24

25

26

27

28

29

30

NOTES

October

1

2

3

4

5

6

7

October

8

9

10

11

12

13

14

15

16

17

18

19

20

21

October

22

23

24

25

26

27

28

29

30

31

NOTES

November

1

2

3

4

5

6

7

NOVEMBER

8

9

10

11

12

13

14

15

16

17

18

19

20

21

NOVEMBER

22

23

24

25

26

27

28

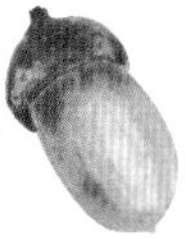

29

30

NOTES

DECEMBER

1

2

3

4

5

6

7

December

8

9

10

11

12

13

14

15

16

17

18

19

20

21

DECEMBER

22

23

24

25

26

27

28

29

30

31

NOTES

The

year

in

review...

January

February

March

April

May

June

July

August

SEPTEMBER

OCTOBER

November

December

NOTES

NOTES